Jim Carrington • Juanbjuan Oliver

Otis the Robot keeps his cool
ISBN: 978-1-85503-605-5

Illustrations by Juanbjuan Oliver / Beehive Illustration

This edition published 2017
10 9 8 7 6 5 4 3 2 1

Printed in the UK by Page Bros (Norwich) Ltd
Designed and typeset by Andy Wilson for Green Desert Ltd

LDA, Findel Education, 2 Gregory Street, Hyde, Cheshire SK14 4HR

www.ldalearning.com

Hi! My name is Otis. I am a robot.

I go to Roboschool every day
except weekends, holidays
and when I'm ill.

This morning,
Mrs A-Bot said,
'I'd like everyone to
sit on the carpet in
one minute's time.'

I finished my activity
and tidied
away.

I have my very own carpet place so I always know **exactly** where to sit.

But when I got to the carpet this morning, it was a **DISASTER**.

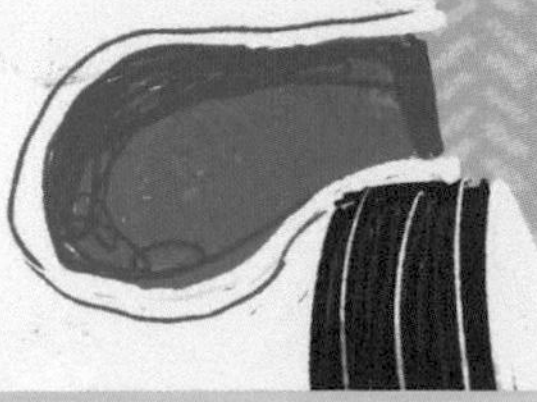

Nina was sitting in ***my*** carpet place.

My circuits **crackled** and **hissed**.
I hit Nina, right on the arm.

'Ow!'
Nina cried.
Miss Mittal, the teaching assistant, took Nina away from the carpet.

'Otis, you shouldn't hit,' Mrs A-Bot said. 'You need to **calm** down.'

'We'll chat about what happened later.'

My circuits **crackled** again.

Later, Marvin was having his reward time. I couldn't join in.

Instead, Mrs A-Bot spoke to me. 'It's okay to feel angry,' she said. 'But you mustn't hit.'

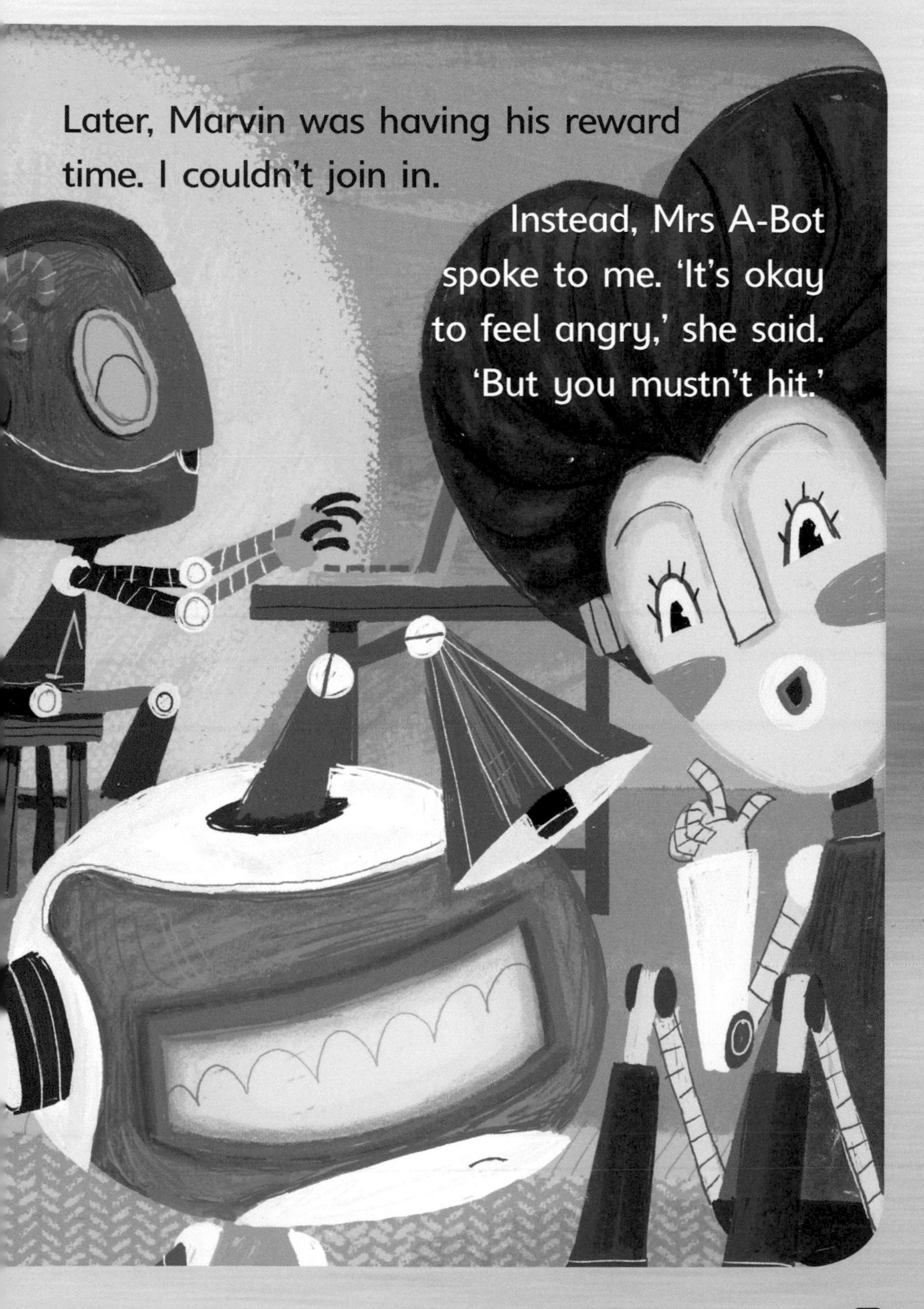

'Nina was in
my space,
though,'
I said.

'You could have asked her to move,' Mrs A-Bot said.

'Or you could have told an adult that you had a problem.'

We read the page in **The Manual** all about hitting.

I felt bad for hitting Nina.
My circuits felt **prickly**.
'Sorry, Nina,' I said.

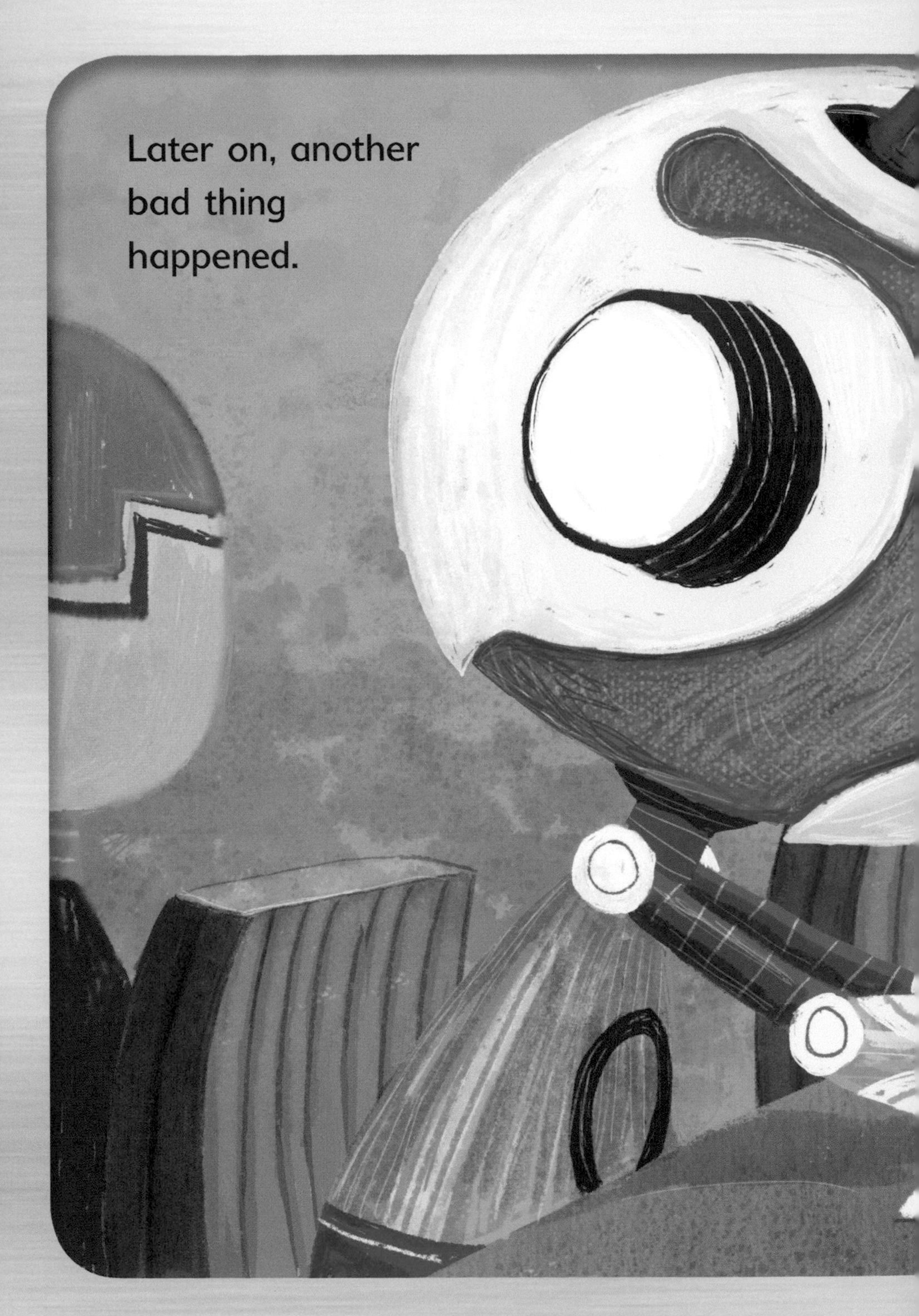

Later on, another
bad thing
happened.

I was
sitting at
my desk
doing some
very excellent
writing.

Then Marvin's arm bumped into me and jogged my hand. It made a **horrible pencil mark** all over my very excellent writing

My circuits **crackled**. I made my fingers into a fist.

But I took
deep breaths
and went to speak
to Miss Mittal.

'Well done for staying **calm** and telling me your problem, Otis,' Miss Mittal said. 'Marvin didn't mean to spoil your work. It was an accident.'

'Sorry, Otis,' Marvin said.

She gave me an eraser and
helped me rub out the pencil mark.

Finishing
my writing
made my
circuits feel
warm and
happy.

What to do when I am angry

(from Otis the Robot keeps his cool)

At school there are lots of things I like and some things that I don't like. There are things that I need to help me, like having my own carpet space.

It is ok to feel angry sometimes. Everybody feels angry sometimes.

One thing that can make me angry is when someone sits in my carpet space.

When people are angry, it is ok to make an angry face.

It is ok to tell someone I am angry.

Sometimes being angry can make people hit others. It isn't ok to hit someone. Being hit will hurt them and they might feel upset. They might cry.

If I feel angry, I will try to calm down and tell an adult what has happened. I can remember that the teacher will sort it out for me. That is the best thing to do.

Brilliant! I can get help to sort things out when I'm angry.